Canadian Jingle Bells

Cover Design by Jennifer Harrington

Printed in Canada by Friesens

Library and Archives Canada Cataloguing in Publication

Townsin, Troy, 1975-
Canadian jingle bells / by Troy Townsin ; illustrated by Jennifer Harrington.

ISBN 978-0-9868892-1-9

1. Christmas stories, Canadian (English).
2. Canada--Juvenile fiction.
I. Harrington, Jennifer, 1973- II. Title.

PS8639.O998C36 2011 jC813'.6 C2011-905387-X

Canadian Jingle Bells

By Troy Townsin
Illustrated by Jennifer Harrington

www.amooseinamapletree.com

Dashing through the snow,
in Santa's flying sleigh,
over Canada we go,
giving gifts along the way!

Everything's lit up,
under the northern lights,
and everywhere in Canada
has such amazing sights!

We see a herd of moose,
out by Dawson City.
The Yukon takes my breath away,
its glaciers are so pretty.

Then up by Yellowknife,
out by a diamond mine,
there's a guy icefishing,
with a big one on the line!

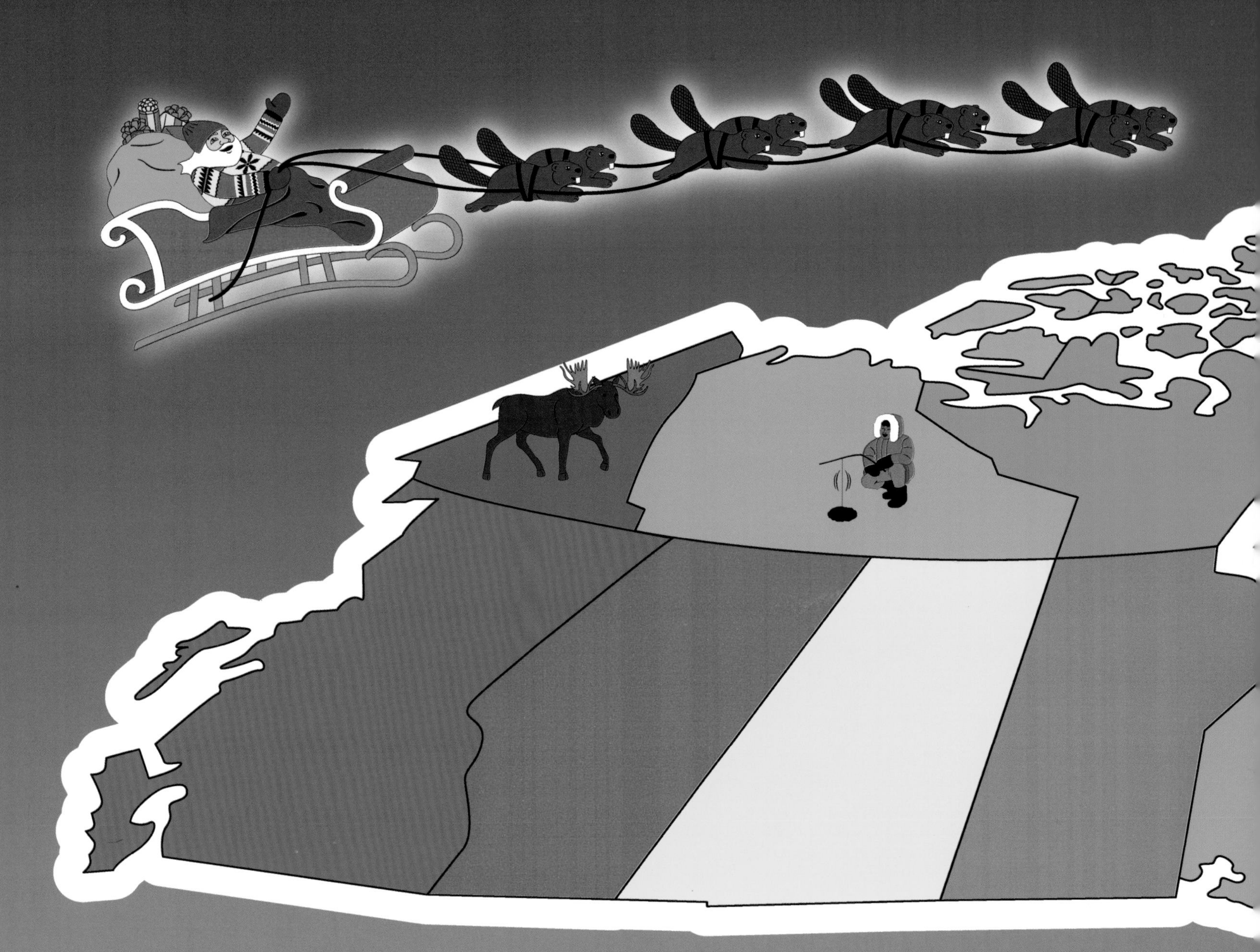

Oh, jingle bells, jingle bells,
jingle all the way,
from Victoria to Halifax,
across the Hudson Bay,

HEY!

Jingle bells, jingle bells,
jingle all the way,

it's Christmas time in Canada,
so Merry Christmas, EH!

HEY!

Jingle bells, jingle bells,
jingle all the way,

it's Christmas time in Canada,
so Merry Christmas, EH!

This book is dedicated to the people of Canada and to all those who visit this wonderful country.

About the Author

Troy Townsin is a proud new Canadian!

Born in Melbourne, Australia, he worked as an actor and playwright before embarking on a round-the-world backpacking extravaganza taking him to several continents. Troy has had many jobs. He has been a Stage Manager in Australia, a Teacher-Trainer in Thailand, a Beverage Manager in the UK, an Information Officer for the United Nations and a Columnist for CBC radio in Canada. Troy has won several awards for his writing, including a prestigious "Travel Writer of the Year" award with TNT Magazine UK and a "Gourmand World Cookbook Award".

Troy fell in love with a Canadian girl, married her and then fell in love with Canada, his new home.

About the Illustrator

Jennifer Harrington is an illustrator and graphic designer who grew up in Vancouver, British Columbia. A trained anthropologist, she decided to follow her childhood passion for the visual arts.

She now lives in Toronto, Ontario, where she runs JSH Graphics, a graphic design company that specializes in corporate branding. Jennifer has illustrated numerous ad campaigns and worked as an art director on magazines in Vancouver, Toronto and London, England.

Others books by Troy and Jennifer:

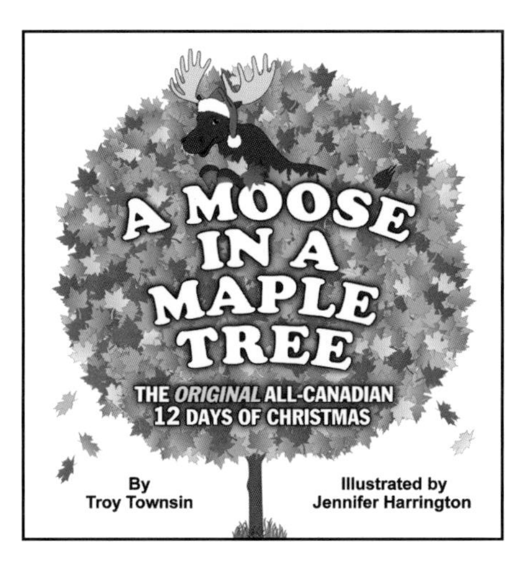

www.amooseinamapletree.com